Frog
on a log

www.autumnchildrensbooks.co.uk

Hop, plop! Hop, plop! Hop went Frog,
out of the pond and on to a log.

He slipped on some moss and could not stop!
Off shot Frog and just went flop!

Frog hopped back <u>o</u>n the l<u>o</u>g, but n<u>o</u>t for l<u>o</u>ng.
That fr<u>o</u>g was cr<u>o</u>ss — what could be wr<u>o</u>ng?

Jog, trot! Jog, trot! Along came a dog.
Back in the pond hopped Frog, from the log.

When the d<u>o</u>g had g<u>o</u>ne, back out p<u>o</u>pped Frog,
looked around and h<u>o</u>pped back <u>o</u>n the l<u>o</u>g.

Now the sun shone down and it got very hot.
And did Frog like that? He did not!

Back in the pond with a hop went Frog.

How will he ever stop on that log?

Frog's h<u>o</u>t and b<u>o</u>thered, but has another try
to st<u>o</u>p <u>o</u>n that l<u>o</u>g, so he can catch a fly.

Will he sp_o_t the one that's just sh_o_t by?

Mucky
pup

Pup liked to jump.
Pup liked to run.

He liked to sl<u>u</u>mp.

For a p<u>u</u>p it was f<u>u</u>n.

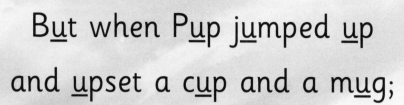

But when Pup jumped up
and upset a cup and a mug;

When he dug in the mud,
then slumped on Mum's rug;

When he gulped down Mum's bun,
and started to munch...

... the crust she had buttered
to have for her lunch;

When he clumped round,
and suddenly upset her stuff;

And tugged at a pillow
and unstuffed the fluff;

When he b<u>u</u>mped back the lid
and j<u>u</u>mped into the tr<u>u</u>nk...

... and just had such fun
tugging out all the junk;

When he r<u>u</u>shed into the pond
and j<u>u</u>mped on a d<u>u</u>ck...

... then that mucky puppy
just ran out of luck!

What do we mean by phonics?

Phonics is the name we give to the links between particular letter patterns in words and the sounds they represent. By drawing children's attention to these links, we provide them with tools to help them work out (or decode) words they have not met before. In other words, we are teaching them to read using phonics.

This is not the only approach to teaching reading, but it has been shown to be particularly helpful in the early stages of learning to read. While some children begin to make the link between sounds and letter patterns for themselves, many need to be taught this clearly. Some research findings suggest that progress in reading is faster when a phonic approach is used in the early stages.

How can this book help?

Each of the books in this series has been designed to focus on a particular group of sounds and their related letter patterns. The rhymes in this book feature two short vowel sounds:

short o as in p<u>o</u>nd, st<u>o</u>p, <u>o</u>nto
short u as in f<u>u</u>n, <u>u</u>pset

You will find the focus sound for each rhyme occurring repeatedly in words in that particular rhyme. The letters used to write the sounds are highlighted in each of those words. As you share the rhymes with your child you will be helping them to make the vital link between particular letters and sounds.

How should I use this book?

Children learn best when the experience is enjoyable. Read the rhymes to your child, sharing the pictures. Talk together about what happens in each rhyme. Now encourage your child to listen as you read the first rhyme again and to try to tell you which sound can be heard in lots of the words. Point out the highlighted sounds in the rhyme, explaining that these are the letters that we use to write the sounds. Help your child to read through the rhyme with you or to try to read it for him or herself.

Titles in the phonics range:

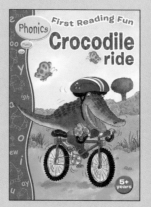